TWELVE DAYS OF CHAOS

Frank Kelly

TWELVE DAYS OF CHAOS

FRANK KELLY

Drawings by

TERRY WILLERS

THE O'BRIEN PRESS
DUBLIN
IRISH AMERICAN BOOK COMPANY (IABC)
BOULDER, COLORADO

First published 1997 by The O'Brien Press Ltd,
20 Victoria Road, Rathgar, Dublin 6, Ireland.

Published in the US and Canada by
The Irish American Book Company
6309 Monarch Park Place
Niwot, Colorado 80503, USA
Telephone (800) 452-7115
Fax (800) 401-9705

1 2 3 4 5 6 7 8 9 10
97 98 99 00 01 02 03 04 05 06

British Library Cataloguing-in-Publication Data

A catalogue reference for this title is
available from the British Library

ISBN: 0-86278-546-4

The O'Brien Press receives assistance from The Arts Council/An Chomhairle Ealaíon

Typesetting, editing, layout, design: The O'Brien Press Ltd
Cover design: Terry Willers
Cover separations: Lithoset Ltd
Printing: Guernsey Press Ltd

I dedicate this book to my wife, Bairbre,
who can always predict my mood swings accurately,
and banish them with
a rubber mallet.

FRANK KELLY believes that if someone really wants to give you something, you should accept it graciously. Although Frank is not Gubnet, he wears a lot of gold rings, and once drove deliberately over a partridge and some swans. He mutters constantly about someone called 'Nuala' in his sleep.

TERRY WILLERS was plucked from adolescent obscurity by Walt Disney, who gave him his first cartooning job, and therefore has a lot to answer for. That was a long time ago. Since then he has produced many near libellous cartoon strips for newspapers, television and comics. *Twelve Days of Chaos* is his latest.

Day 1

Dear Nuala,

Thank you very much
for your lovely present
of a Partridge in a Pear Tree.

We're getting the hang of feeding the Partridge now,
although it was difficult at first
to win its confidence.
It bit the Mother rather badly in the hand,
but they're good friends now
and we're keeping the Pear Tree indoors
in a bucket.

Thank you again.

Yours affectionately,

Gubnet O'Lunacy

Day 2

Dear Nuala,

I cannot tell you how surprised we were
to hear from you so soon again
and to receive your lovely present of
Two Turtle Doves.
You really are *too* kind.

At first the Partridge was very jealous
and suspicious of the Doves
and they had a terrible row
on the night the Doves arrived.

We had to send for the vet,
but the birds are OK now and the
stitches are due to come out
in a week or two.

The vet's bill was eight pound,
but the Mother is over her annoyance,
and the Doves and the Partridge
are watching the telly from the
Pear Tree as I write.

Yours ever,

Gubnet

Day 3

Dear Nuala,

We must be foremost in your thoughts.
I had only posted my letter when
the Three French Hens arrived.

There was another sort out between the
Hens and the Doves who sided with
the Partridge,
and the vet had to be
sent for again.

The Mother was raging 'cos the bill
was *sixteen pound* this time,
but she has almost cooled down.
However, the fact that the birds' droppings
keep falling on her hair while she's watchin' telly
doesn't help matters.

Thanking you for your kindness,

I remain

your Gubnet

Day 4

Dear Nuala,

You mustn't have received my last letter
when you were sending us
Four Calling Birds.

There was pandemonium in the
Pear Tree again last night and the
vet's bill was **thirty-two pound**.
The Mother is on sedation as I write.

I know that you meant no harm
and remain your close friend,

Gubnet

Day 5

Nuala,

Your generosity knows no bounds:
Five Gold Rings.

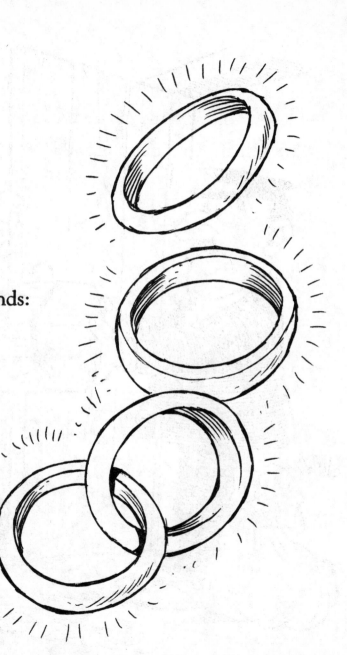

When the parcel arrived I was scared stiff
that it might be more birds
because the smell in the living-room
is *atrocious*.
However I don't want to seem
ungrateful for the
beautiful rings.

Your affectionate friend,
Gubnet

Day 6

Nuala,

What are you trying to *do* to us?
It isn't that we don't appreciate your
generosity, but the Six Geese have not
alone nearly murdered the Calling Birds,
but they laid their eggs on top of
the vet's head from the Pear Tree.

And his bill was **sixty-eight pound in cash**.

The Mother is munching

sixty grains of Valium a day

and talking to herself

in a most alarming way,

You **must** keep your feelings

for me in check,

Gubnet

Day 7

Nuala,

*We are not amused by your **little** joke.*
Seven Swans-a-Swimming
is a most romantic idea,
but not in the bath
of a private house.

29

We cannot use the bathroom now
because they have gone completely savage
and rush the door
every time we try to enter.

If things go on this way the Mother and I
will smell as bad as the living-room carpet.

Please

    lay off

it is NOT *fair.*

Gubnet

Day 8

Nuala,

Who *the* hell do you think gave you the right
to send Eight hefty Maids-a-Milking here
to eat us out of house and home?

Their cattle is all over the front lawn
and has trampled the hell out of
the Mother's rose beds.

The Swans invaded the living-room in a sneak attack
and the ensuing battle between them and the
Calling Birds, Turtle Doves, French Hens
and Partridge made the Battle of
the Somme look like a meditation class.

The Mother is on a bottle of whiskey a day
as well as the sixty grains of Valium.

I'm VERY *annoyed with you.*

Gubnet

Day 9

Listen, You Louser!

There's enough pandemonium in this place night and day without Nine Drummers Drumming ...

while the Eight flaming Maids-a-Milking is beatin'
me poor old alcoholic Mother out of the kitchen
and gobbling everything in sight.

I'm warning you,

you're making an ENEMY

out of me!

Gubnet

Day 10

Listen, MANURE-Face!

I hope you'll be haunted by the strains of the Ten Pipers Piping ...

that you sent to torment us last night.

They were aided in their evil work by
those maniac Drummers
and it wasn't a pleasant sight
to look out the window
and to see Eight hefty
Maids-a-Milking pogo-ing round to
the ensuing punk rock uproar.

The Mother has just finished her third bottle of whiskey on top of a hundred-and-twenty-four grains of Valium.

You'll get YOURS!

Gubnet O'Lunacy

Day 11

You have **SCANDALISED** my mother,

You Dirty Jezebel!

It was bad enough to have
Eight Maids-a-Milking dancing to
punk music on the front lawn,
but they have been joined by their
friends, the Eleven Lords-a-Leaping ...

and the antics of the whole lot of them
would leave the most decadent days
of the Roman Empire look like
the Shrine of Fatima.

I'll get you yet,
ya OULD BAG.

Day 12

Listen, Slurry-Head,
you have RUINED our lives.

The Twelve Maidens dancin' turned up last night and beat the daylights out of the Eight Maids-a-Milking 'cos they found them **CARRYING ON** with the Eleven Lords-a-Leaping.

Meanwhile the Swans got out of the living-room
where they'd been hidin'
since the big battle and **SAVAGED HELL**
out of the Lords and all the Maids.
There were eight ambulances here
last night and the
local civil defence as well.

58

The Mother is in a home for the bewildered
and I'm here up to me neck in birds' droppings,
empty whiskey and Valium bottles,
birds' blood and feathers while the
flamin' cows eat the leaves off
the Pear Tree.

I'm a BROKEN man!